A DOZEN A FLUTE SONGBOOK
Christmas

THE WILLIS MUSIC COMPANY

Good King Wenceslas

Words by John Mason Neale
Music Traditional Finnish
Arranged by Christopher Hussey

**TRACKS
1–2**

Watch out for...

- The time signature $\frac{4}{4}$ — this tells you there are four quarter note beats in each measure.

- The dynamic marks, which tell you how loudly or softly to play.
  p = *piano*, tells you to play 'softly'.   ***f*** = *forte*, tells you to play 'loudly'.

- Your articulation — try to play smoothly in a *legato* style.

Confidently

(Introduction)   *f* Good   King   Wen - ces - las   looked   out

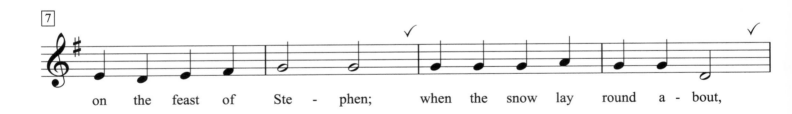

on   the   feast   of   Ste - phen;   when   the   snow   lay   round   a - bout,

deep   and   crisp   and   e - ven.   Bright - ly   shone   the   moon   that   night,

though   the   frost   was   cru - el;   when   a   poor   man   came   in   sight,

3

gath - 'ring win - ter fu - - el.

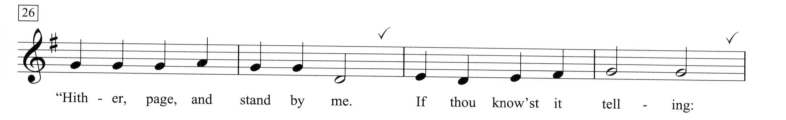

"Hith - er, page, and stand by me. If thou know'st it tell - ing:

yon - der peas - ant, who is he? Where and what his dwell - ing?"

"Sire, he lives a good league hence, un - der - neath the moun - tain,

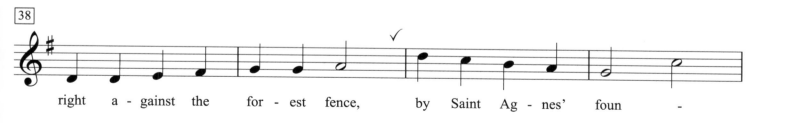

right a - gainst the for - est fence, by Saint Ag - nes' foun -

-tain." *p*

Infant Holy, Infant Lowly

Traditional Polish
Arranged by Christopher Hussey

 TRACKS
3–4

𝄢 *Watch out for...*

- The time signature **3/4** — this tells you there are three quarter note beats in each measure.

- The dotted half notes — which last three beats, and the eighth notes — which last for half a beat and can be joined as a pair like this:

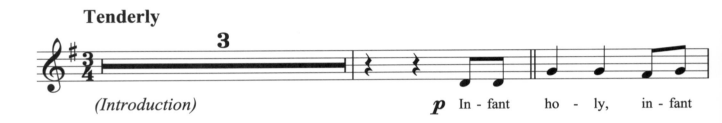

Tenderly

(Introduction)

p In - fant ho - ly, in - fant

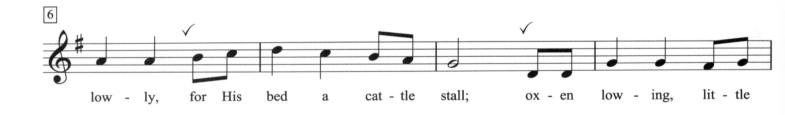

low - ly, for His bed a cat - tle stall; ox - en low - ing, lit - tle

know - ing Christ, the Babe, is Lord of all. Swift are wing - ing, an - gels

sing - ing, no - wells ring - ing, ti - dings bring - ing: Christ, the Babe, is Lord of

18

all.

3

f Flocks were

23

sleep - ing, shep - herds keep - ing vig - il till the mor - ning

26

new saw the glor - y, heard the stor - y, ti - dings of a gos - pel

30

true. Thus re - joi - cing, free from sor - row, prais - es

33

voi - cing greet the mor - row: Christ, the Babe, was born for you.

p

In The Bleak Midwinter

Words by Christina Rossetti
Music by Gustav Holst
Arranged by Christopher Hussey

TRACKS
5–6

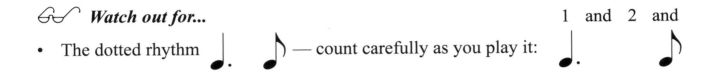

Watch out for...

- The dotted rhythm ♩. ♪ — count carefully as you play it:

  1 and 2 and
  ♩. ♪

- Your articulation — play smoothly, in a *legato* style, and keep your tone warm so that the music still sounds 'tender' even when you are playing f (*forte*).

Tenderly

f In   the   bleak   mid - win - ter,   frost - y   wind   made

moan,   earth   stood   hard   as   i -   ron,

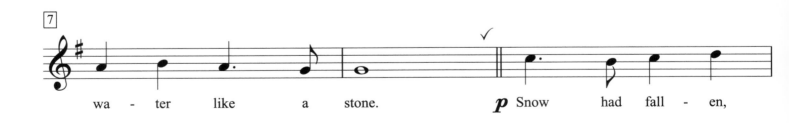

wa - ter   like   a   stone. p Snow   had   fall - en,

snow   on   snow,   snow_____   on_____   snow.

Hark! The Herald Angels Sing

Words by Charles Wesley
Music by Felix Mendelssohn
Arranged by Christopher Hussey

**TRACKS
7–8**

𝄞 **Watch out for...**

- The two-note slurs in this song 𝅘𝅥𝅘𝅥 — join these notes together as smoothly as possible.

- The octave leaps in measures 12–13, 28–29 and 36–37.

Gracefully

(Introduction) *p* Hark! The her - ald an - gels sing,___ "Glor - y to the

new - born King! Peace on earth and mer - cy mild,___ God and sin - ners

re - con - ciled." Joy - ful, all you na - tions rise,___ join the tri - umph

of the skies;___ with th'an - gel - ic host pro - claim: "Christ is___ born in

Silent Night

Words by Joseph Mohr
Music by Franz Gruber
Arranged by Christopher Hussey

 TRACKS 9–10

🎼 ***Watch out for...***

- The dotted rhythm ♩. ♪ — count carefully as you play it: 1 and 2 and ♩. ♪

- The breath marks — they are less frequent now, only once every four measures. You can add more in, if you find the phrases too long for one breath.

Peacefully

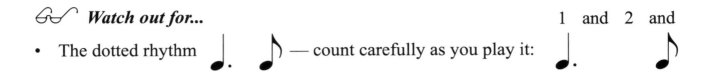

(Introduction) ***p*** Si - lent night, ho - ly

night. All is calm, all is bright,

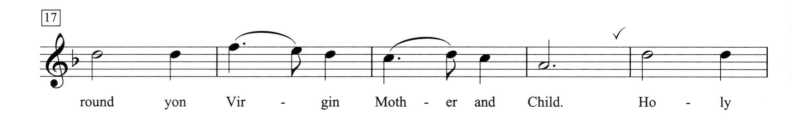

round yon Vir - gin Moth - er and Child. Ho - ly

In - fant so ten - der and mild, sleep in heav - en - ly

It Came Upon The Midnight Clear

Words by Edmund Sears
Music by Richard Storrs Willis
Arranged by Christopher Hussey

 TRACKS 11–12

𝄞 **Watch out for...**

- The new dymanic marks — **mp** = *mezzo piano*, telling you to play 'moderately softly', and **mf** = *mezzo forte*, telling you to play 'moderately loudly'.

- The *accidentals* in measures 22 and 54 — the *sharp* sign ♯ tells you to raise the pitch of the note that follows it by a *half step*.

Ding Dong! Merrily On High

Words by George Ratcliffe Woodward
Music Traditional
Arranged by Christopher Hussey

**TRACKS
13–14**

Watch out for...

- The four-note slurs in this song 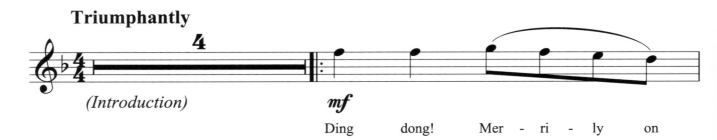 — join this group of eighth notes together as smoothly as possible.

- The very long six-bar phrase in measures 13–18 and 29–34 — if you're finding them tricky to play in one breath, add some more breaths while you build up to it.

- The *repeat* signs ‖: :‖ — when you reach the 'end repeat' in measure 20, repeat back from the 'start repeat' in measure 5, and play on.

Triumphantly

(Introduction)   *mf*

Ding   dong!   Mer - ri - ly   on

high,   in   heav'n   the   bells   are   ring   -   ing.

Ding   dong!   Ver - i - ly   the   sky   is   riv'n   with   an - gels   sing   -   ing.

Glor - - - - - - - - - - - - - - - - - -

- - - - - - - - i - a, Ho -

- san - na in ex - cel - sis! Pray you, du - ti - ful - ly

prime your mat - in chime, ye ring - ers. May you beau - ti - ful - ly

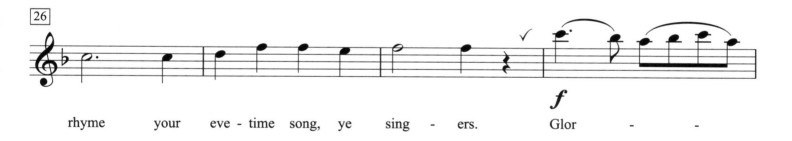

rhyme your eve - time song, ye sing - ers. Glor - -

- - - - - - - -

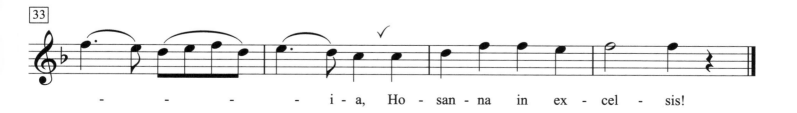

- - - - i - a, Ho - san - na in ex - cel - sis!

Go Tell It On The Mountain

Words by John W. Work
Music Traditional African-American
Arranged by Christopher Hussey

**TRACKS
15–16**

𝒢𝓈 ***Watch out for...***

- The four-note slurs — join these notes together as smoothly as possible.

- The syncopated rhythms — practise these measures on their own and slowly to begin with, counting carefully as you play:

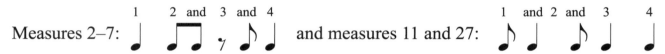

Measures 2–7: [rhythm notation with counts: 1 2 and 3 and 4] and measures 11 and 27: [rhythm notation with counts: 1 and 2 and 3 4]

Joyfully

mf

f Go, tell it on the moun - tain,

o - ver the hills and ev - 'ry - where,_____ go, tell it on the

The First Nowell

Traditional English
Arranged by Christopher Hussey

TRACKS 17–18

👓 ***Watch out for...***

- The *anacruses* in this song — an *anacrusis* or *pickup* is a note (or group of notes) at the beginning of a phrase that precedes the downbeat of the first full measure of that phrase. You'll find examples of this on the last beat of measure 1 into 2, and at the beginning of the tune on the last beat of measure 8 into 9 — and indeed starting almost every four-measure phrase. Can you spot some examples of an anacrusis in earlier songs?

- The *repeat* signs ‖: :‖ , the *first time bar* |¹·_____| and *second time bar.* |²·_____

  When you reach the 'end repeat' at the end of the first time bar (measure 32), repeat back from the 'start repeat' in measure 9. This time, when you get to the first time bar, miss it out, and jump to the second time bar and play on.

- The *fermata* 𝄐 on the last note — this tells you to hold the note for longer than its written duration.

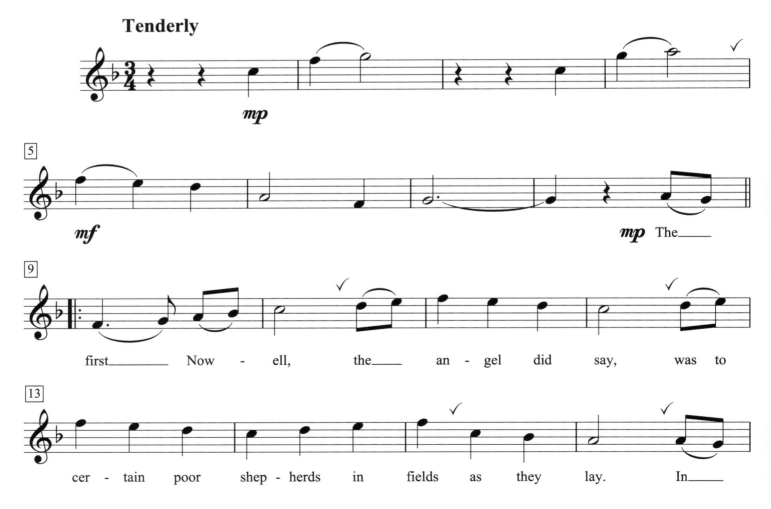

Huron Carol

Traditional Canadian
Arranged by Christopher Hussey

**TRACKS
19–20**

⌒⌒ ***Watch out for...***

- The changes of time signature between $\frac{4}{4}$ and $\frac{3}{4}$ — be sure to count carefully so that you play the music correctly.

- The dynamic marks — this song uses ***p*** , ***mp***, ***mf*** and ***f***, so watch out for each change and you'll find they help to make your playing more expressive.

- The key — this is the first song in this collection to be in a *minor* key: A minor.

Thoughtfully

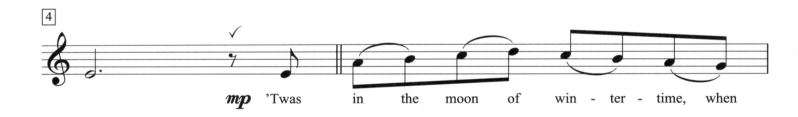

We Wish You A Merry Christmas

Traditional English
Arranged by Christopher Hussey

**TRACKS
21–22**

🎵 ***Watch out for...***

- The articulation marks — *staccato* marks ♩ , *tenuto* marks ♩ and *accents* ♩ are used in this song, and there's also a passage marked *legato* (smoothly). Making the difference between these types of articulation clear will give your performance more detail and character.

- The **D.C. al Coda** — when you reach this instruction, repeat the music from the beginning until **To Coda** ⊕ , then jump to the *coda*, marked ⊕ **CODA** , and play to the end.

Joyfully and crisply

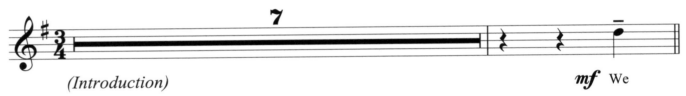

(Introduction)

mf We

wish you a mer - ry Christ - mas, we wish you a mer - ry Christ - mas, we

wish you a mer - ry Christ - mas and a hap - py New Year! Good

ti - dings we bring to you and your kin; we

Rocking Carol

TRACKS
23–24

Words by Percy Dearmer
Music Traditional Czech
Arranged by Christopher Hussey

Watch out for...

- The *accidentals* — some of the Gs in this melody have a ♯ before them, which isn't part of the key signature. The G naturals in the bars immediately following a G sharp have a 'cautionary' natural before them (♮), to remind you that they aren't to be played as sharps.

- The *hairpins* — this sign ◁ indicates a **crescendo** for its duration, while ▷ indicates a **diminuendo**. These will add expression to your performance.

Gently, with expression

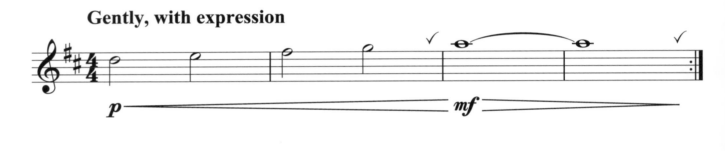

p   *mf*

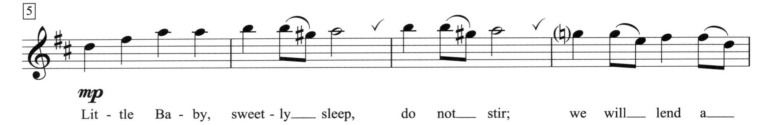

mp
Lit - tle Ba - by, sweet - ly__ sleep, do not__ stir; we will__ lend a__

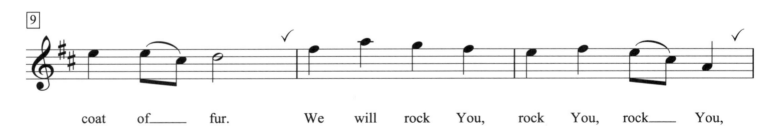

coat of__ fur. We will rock You, rock You, rock__ You,

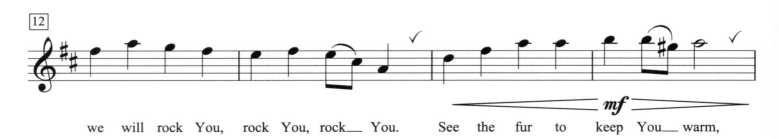

we will rock You, rock You, rock__ You. See the fur to keep You__ warm,

mf

25

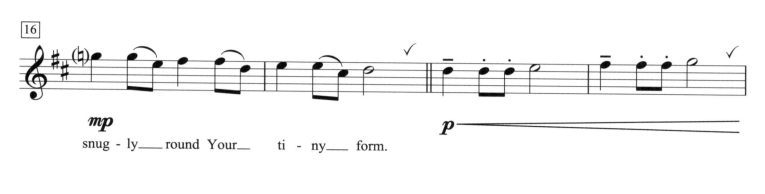

snug - ly___ round Your___ ti - ny___ form.

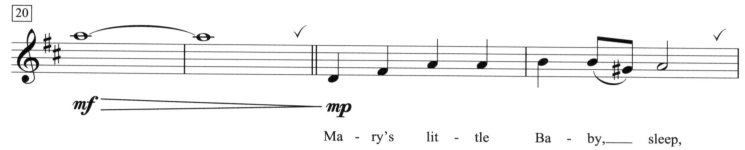

Ma - ry's lit - tle Ba - by,___ sleep,

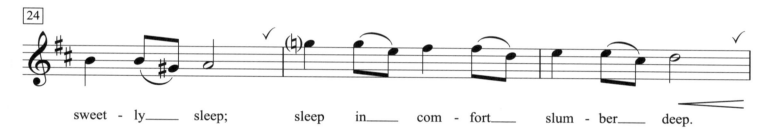

sweet - ly___ sleep; sleep in___ com - fort___ slum - ber___ deep.

We will rock You, rock You, rock___ You, we will rock You, rock You, rock___ You.

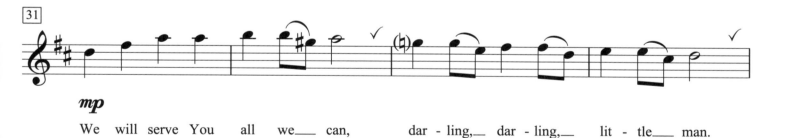

We will serve You all we___ can, dar - ling,___ dar - ling,___ lit - tle___ man.

Joy To The World

Words by Isaac Watts
Music by Lowell Mason (based on themes
from 'Messiah' by George Frideric Handel)
Arranged by Christopher Hussey

**TRACKS
25–26**

⚮ *Watch out for...*

- The time signature — **2/4** tells you there are two quarter note beats in each measure.

- The sixteenth notes ♪ — which last for a quarter of a beat and can be joined in groups like this: ♫ or ♬

- The dotted eighth note-sixteenth note rhythm: ♩. ♪ Practise this rhythm on its own to begin with.

Chirpily

(Introduction)   *mf*

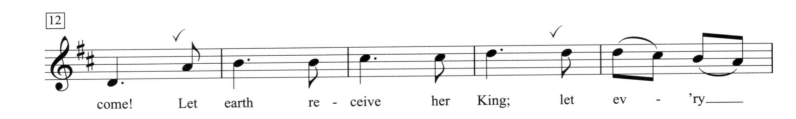

Joy   to   the   world,   the   Lord   is

come!   Let   earth   re - ceive   her   King;   let   ev - 'ry_____

heart_____   pre - pare_____   Him_____   room,_____   and   heav'n   and   Na - ture_____

I Saw Three Ships

Traditional English
Arranged by Christopher Hussey

TRACKS 27–28

Watch out for...

- The time signature $\frac{6}{8}$ — this tells you there are six eighth notes in each measure.

Unlike $\frac{3}{4}$ which also has six eighth notes in each measure, in $\frac{6}{8}$ the quavers are grouped in threes, so that there are two dotted quarter note beats in each measure. This is an example of a *compound meter*.

- The articulation in the last four measures.

With a lilt

(Introduction) mf I saw three ships come

sail - ing in on Christ - mas Day, on Christ - mas Day, I

saw three ships come sail - ing in on Christ - mas Day in the

mor - ning. And what was in those

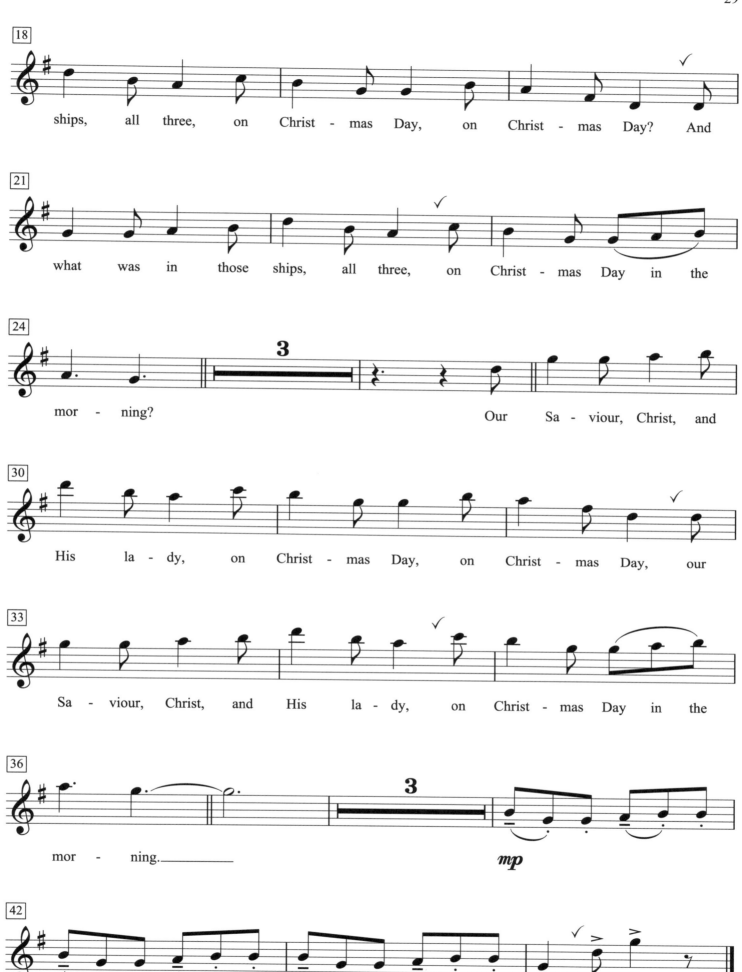

Here We Come A-Wassailing

Traditional English
Arranged by Christopher Hussey

**TRACKS
29–30**

✎ *Watch out for...*

- The changes between the *compound meter* **6/8** and the *simple meters* **2/4** and **4/4**.

  The signs at the time signature changes — ♩.=♩ and ♩=♩. — show us that the beat (or *pulse*) stays the same. There is simply a change of 'feel' as we move from the beat being subdivided into three eighth notes (in the compound meter) to two eighth notes (in the simple meters).

- The articulation in the last measure.

Joyously, with a bounce

CD Track Listing

Exclusive Distributors:
Music Sales Limited
Newmarket Road, Bury St Edmunds, Suffolk IP33 3YB, UK.
Music Sales Pty Limited
Units 3-4, 17 Willfox Street, Condell Park NSW 2200, Australia.

Order No. WMR101420
ISBN: 978-1-78305-646-0

Edited by Sam Lung.
Exercises written by Christopher Hussey.
Music engraved by Camden Music Services.
Backing tracks composed and arranged by Christopher Hussey and Jeremy Birchall.
Flute by Anna Stokes.
CD recorded, mixed and mastered by Imogen Hall and Jonas Persson.

Printed in the EU.